Ukulele *from the* Begin

Pop Songs

The Yellow Book

CHESTER MUSIC

Published by
Chester Music
14-15 Berners Street,
London W1T 3LJ, UK.

Exclusive Distributors:
Music Sales Limited
Distribution Centre, Newmarket Road,
Bury St Edmunds, Suffolk IP33 3YB, UK.

Music Sales Corporation
180 Madison Avenue, 24th Floor,
New York NY 10016, USA.

Music Sales Pty Limited
Units 3-4, 17 Willfox Street, Condell Park
NSW 2200, Australia.

Order No. CH82544
ISBN 978-1-78305-628-6

Book content and layout by Camden Music.
Compiled by Christopher Hussey.
Edited by Toby Knowles.

Printed in the EU.

www.musicsales.com

About the series

This songbook uses the chords and picking patterns taught in *Ukulele from the Beginning Book 2*. As well as making this an ideal companion book for anyone working through the *Ukulele from the Beginning* course, *Pop Songs: The Yellow Book* is also an enjoyable standalone song collection for anyone learning to play the ukulele.

Contents

Page	Song title	Chords used	Introduction of new chord
4	*About this book/Fingerpicking patterns*		
5	*Chord Library*		
6	**Roar** Katy Perry	Am, F, C, Dm	**Am, F, C, Dm**
8	**Just Give Me A Reason** Pink feat. Nate Ruess	F, C, Dm, Am, C7	**C7**
9	**Light Me Up** Birdy	C, G, Am, F	**G**
10	**Stay** Rihanna feat. Mikky Ekko	F, Dm, Am, G, C	
12	**Panic Cord** Gabrielle Aplin	F, C, Dm, Am, G	
14	**I'm Yours** Jason Mraz	C, G, Am, F, D7	**D7**
16	**Hit The Road Jack** Ray Charles	E7, Am, F	**E7**
17	**Story Of My Life** One Direction	F, B♭, Dm	**B♭**
18	**Right Place Right Time** Olly Murs	F, Gm, B♭	**Gm**
20	**I Knew You Were Trouble** Taylor Swift	F, C, Dm, B♭	
22	**Pompeii** Bastille	B♭, F, Dm, C	
24	**Let Her Go** Passenger	C, B♭, F, Dm	
26	**Wrecking Ball** Miley Cyrus	Dm, F, C, Gm, B♭	
28	**Burn** Ellie Goulding	C, Dm, B♭, Am, F	
30	**...Baby One More Time** Britney Spears	Dm, A, F, Gm, B♭, C	**A**
32	**Counting Stars** OneRepublic	Dm, F, C, B♭	

About this book

Here's a great selection of pop songs to add to your repertoire! They use only what you have learnt in *Ukulele From The Beginning Books 1* and *2*, featuring many of the chords that you know by the end of *Book 2*, as well as some of the fingerpicking patterns you have been taught.

Below are the fingerpicking patterns that you'll need for songs in this book, and opposite is a library of all the chords used.

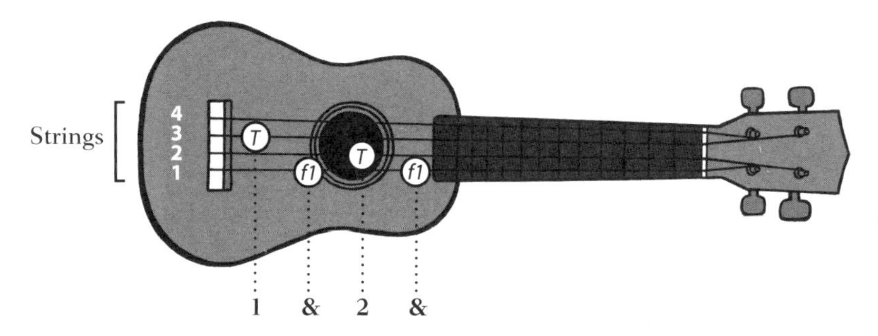

which can be written:

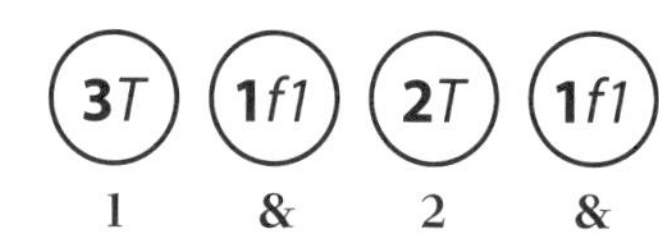

Play this pattern twice when there are 4 beats in the bar:

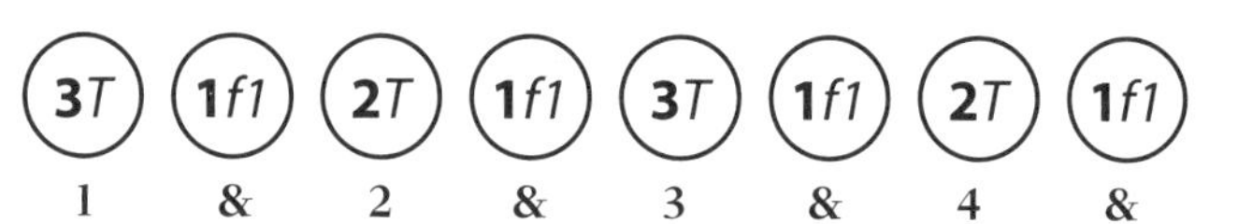

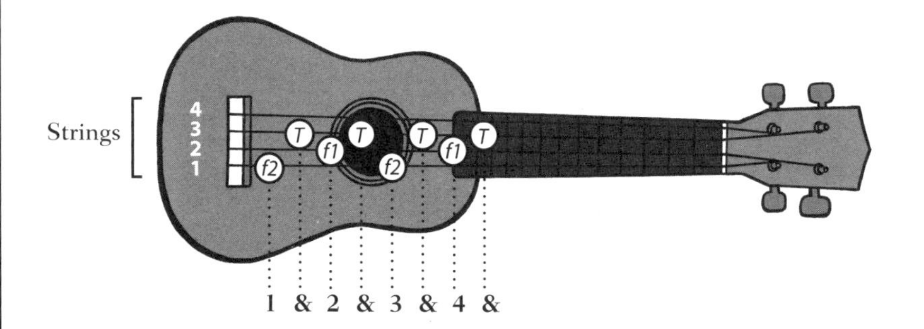

which can be written:

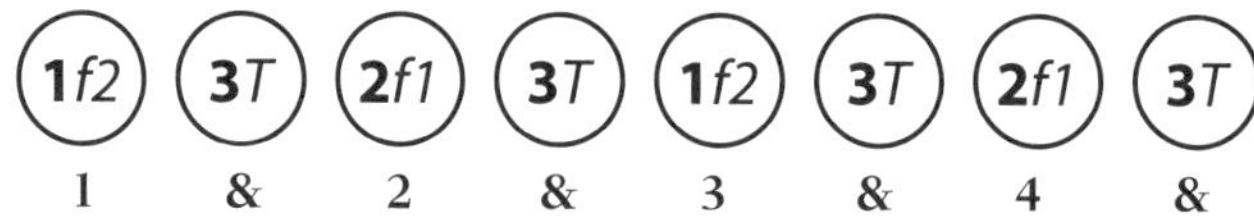

Chord Library

Am

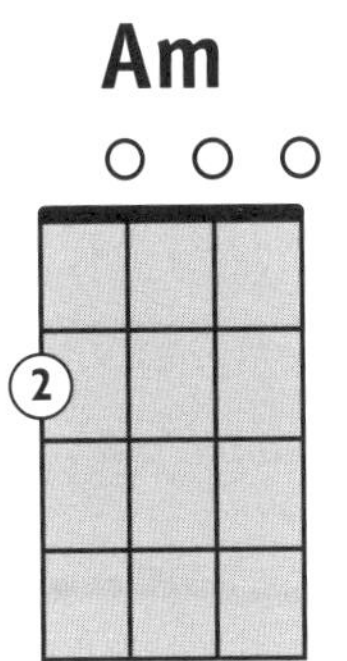

F

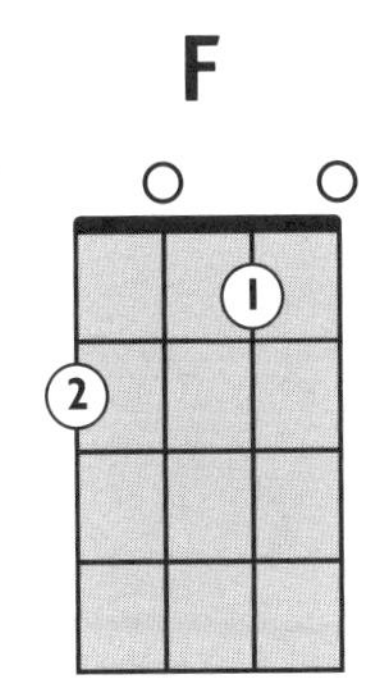

C

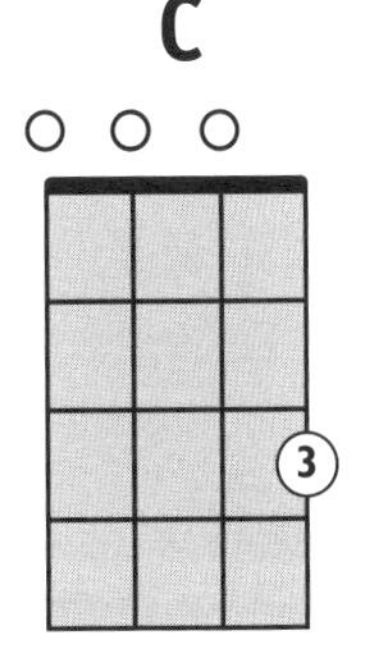

Dm

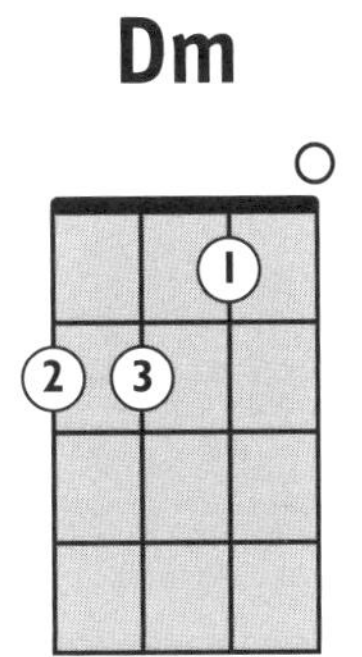

C7

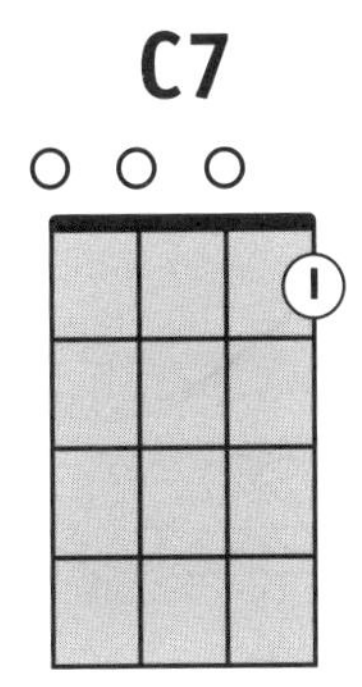

G

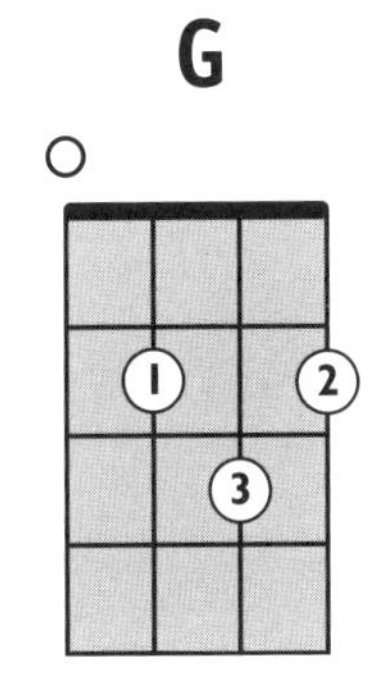

D7

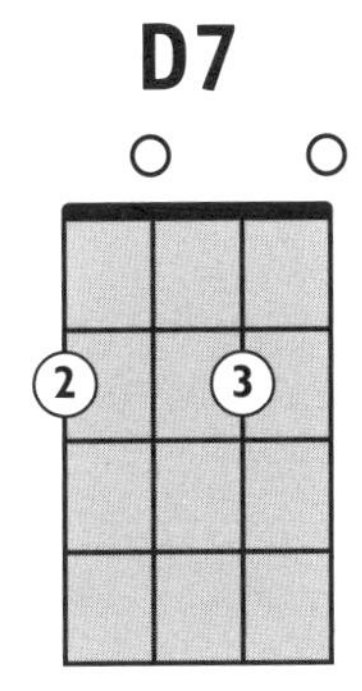

E7

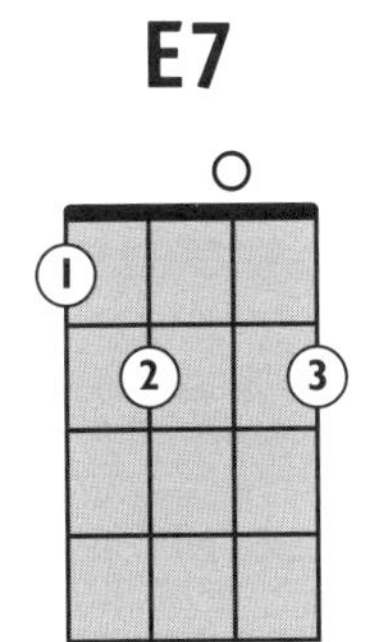

B♭

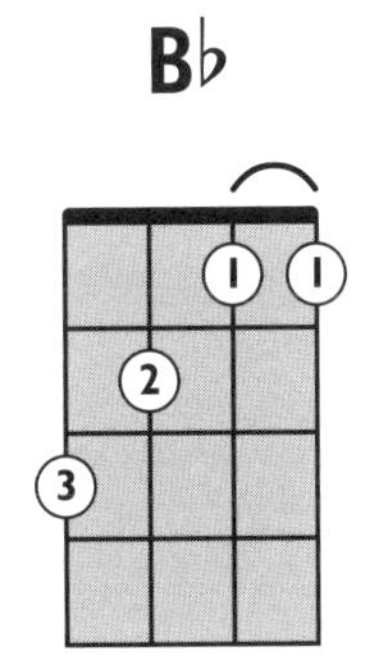

Gm

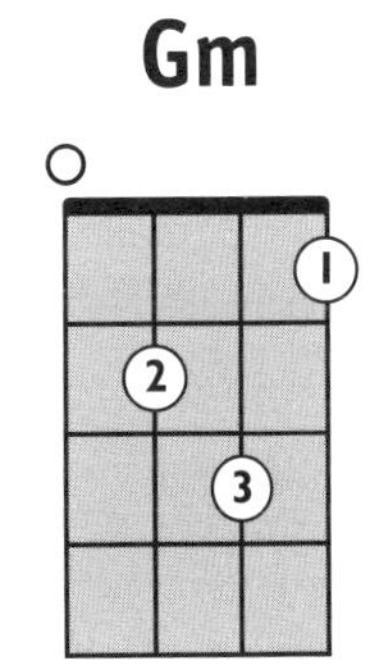

A

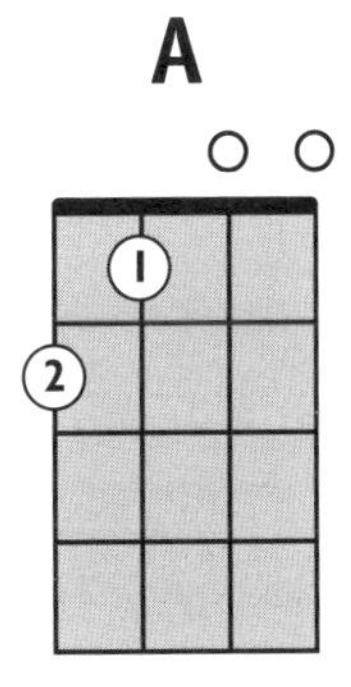

Roar

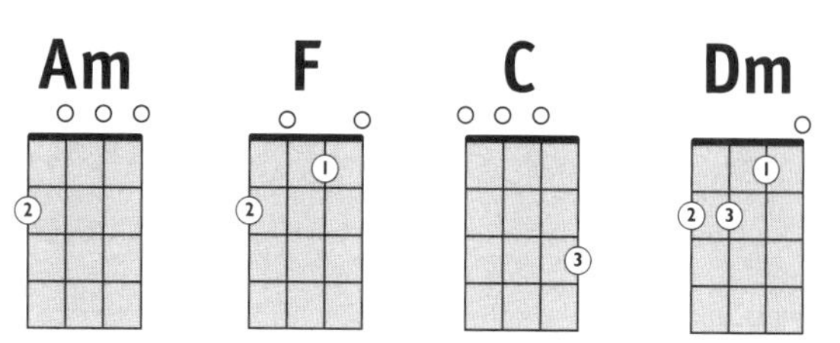

Words & Music by Katy Perry, Lukasz Gottwald, Bonnie McKee,
Max Martin & Henry Russell Walter

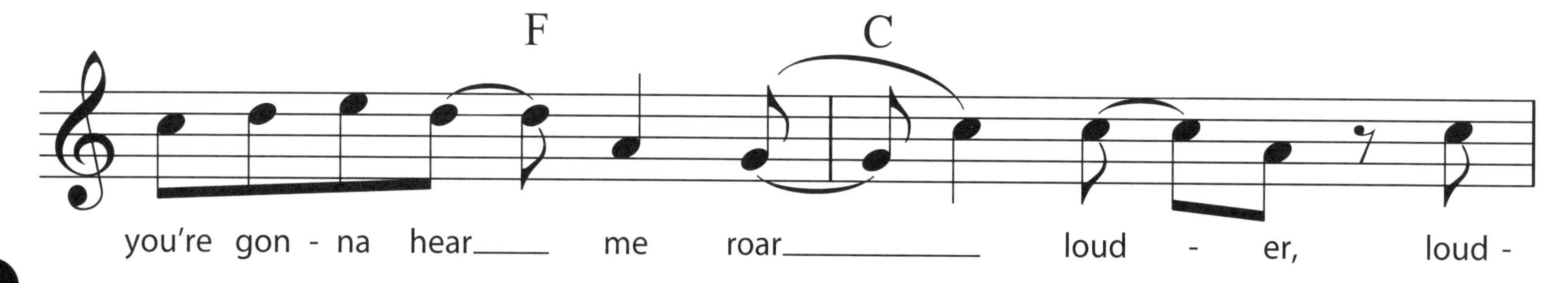

Dm
Am
-er than a li - on, 'cause I___ am a cham - pion and
F
C
you're gon - na hear___ me roar.___ Oh oh oh oh oh,___
Dm
Am
oh___ oh oh oh oh oh,___ oh___ oh oh oh oh oh,___
F
C
you're gon - na hear___ me roar.___

Just Give Me A Reason
Words & Music by Alecia Moore, Jeff Bhasker & Nate Ruess
© Copyright 2012 Sony/ATV Songs LLC/Pink Inside Publishing/Way Above Music/
W B Music Corp/EMI Blackwood Music Inc/FBR Music/Bearvon Music
EMI Music Publishing Limited/Sony/ATV Music Publishing/Warner/Chappell North America
Limited. All Rights Reserved. International Copyright Secured.
F C Dm Am C7
1 & 2 & 3 & 4 &
F C
Just give me a rea - son, just a lit - tle bit's e - nough. Just a
Dm Am C7
sec - ond, we're not bro - ken, just bent, and we can learn to love a - gain.
F C
It's in the stars, it's been writ - ten in the scars on our hearts:
Dm Am C7 F
we're not bro - ken, just bent, and we can learn to love a - gain.

Light Me Up
Words & Music by Thomas Hull & Jasmine Van den Bogaerde
© Copyright 2013 Good Soldier Songs Limited.
Universal Music Publishing Limited/Warner/Chappell Music Publishing Limited.
All Rights Reserved. International Copyright Secured.
C G Am F
1 & 2 & 3 & 4 &
C G Am
You light me up when all I see is dark - ness, you
C G Am
light me up when I'm down. And if I
F G Am C
fall a - part, you know where to find my piec - es,
F G Am
when they can't be found. You

Stay

Words & Music by Justin Parker & Mikky Ekko

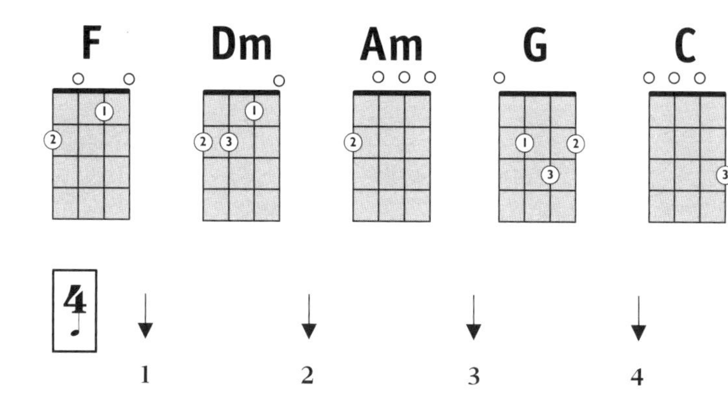

C
Dm
Am
Not real-ly sure how to feel a-bout it. Some-thing in the way you move
F
C
Dm
makes me feel like I can't live with-out you. Yeah, it
Am
F
C
Dm
takes me all the way: I want you to stay.
Am
C
Am
C
Am

Panic Cord

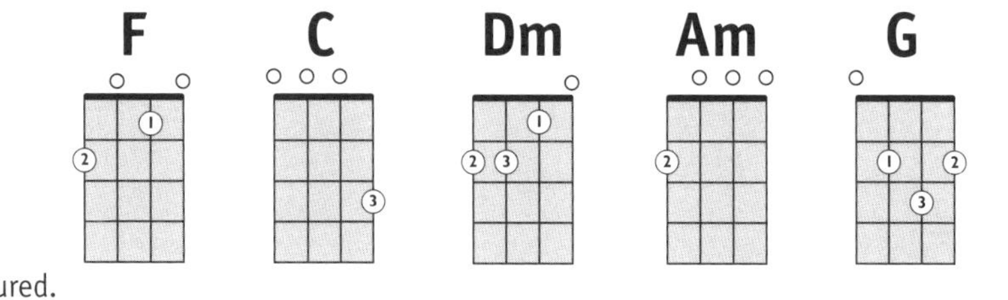

Words & Music by Jez Ashurst, Gabrielle Aplin & Nicholas Atkinson

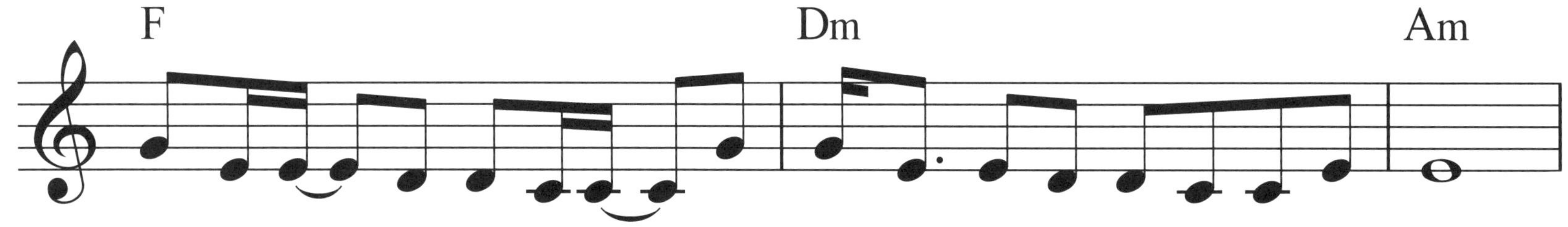

G
F
Dm
Oh,
we're just a box of sou-ven-irs.
'Cause
Am
F
C
G
Am
F
may - be
I pulled the pan - ic cord, and may - be
C
G
Am
F
you were hap - py, I was bored. May-be I want - ed you to change;
C
G
Am
F
C
may - be I'm the one to blame.

I'm Yours

Words & Music by Jason Mraz

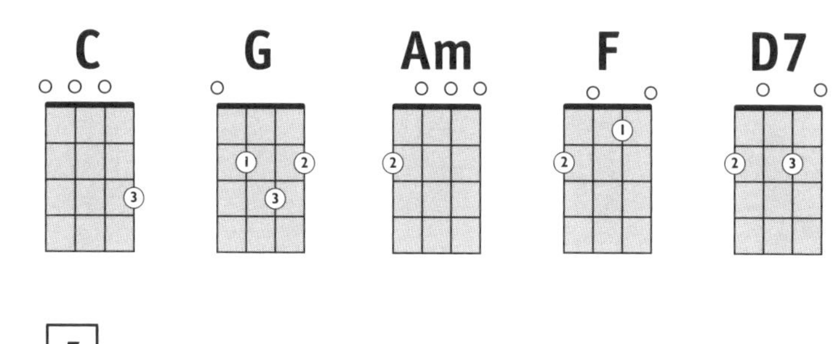

Swung

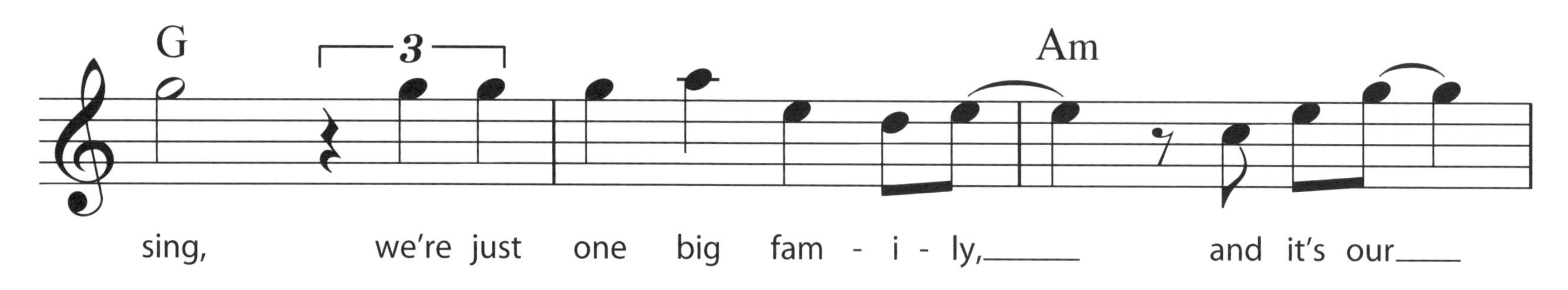

D7 C
loved. So, I won't hes - i -
G Am
-tate no more, no more, it can - not
F 3 C
wait. I'm sure there's no need to com - plic -
G Am
- ate, our time is short, this is our
F C
fate: I'm yours.

Hit The Road Jack
Words & Music by Percy Mayfield
© Copyright 1961 Tangerine Music Corporation, USA.
Kassner Associated Publishers Limited.
All Rights Reserved. International Copyright Secured.
E7
Am
F
1
2
3
4
Swung
E7 Am F E7
Hit the road, Jack, and don't you come back no
Am F E7 Am
more, no more, no more, no more, hit the road, Jack, and
F E7 Am
don't you come back no more.
1. F E7
What d'you say? Hit the
2. Am
16

Story Of My Life
Words & Music by John Ryan, Jamie Scott, Julian Bunetta, Harry Styles, Niall Horan, Liam Payne, Louis Tomlinson & Zayn Malik
© Copyright 2013 BMG Platinum Songs US/Holy Cannoli Music/Music Of Big Deal/Bob Erotik Music/The Family Songbook.
EMI Music Publishing Limited/Universal/MCA Music Limited/
BMG Rights Management (US) LLC/PPM Music Ltd.
All Rights Reserved. International Copyright Secured.
F
B♭
Dm
1 & 2 & 3 & 4 &
F
The stor - y of my life; I
take her home, I
give her hope, I
B♭
Dm
drive all night to keep her warm, and time is
spend her love un - til she's broke in - side:
1. B♭
F
fro - - zen. The
2. B♭
F
the stor - y of my life.

Right Place Right Time

Words & Music by Stephen Robson, Claude Kelly & Oliver Murs

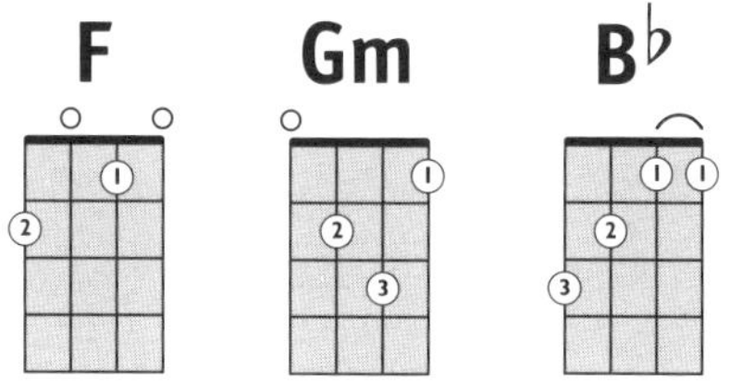

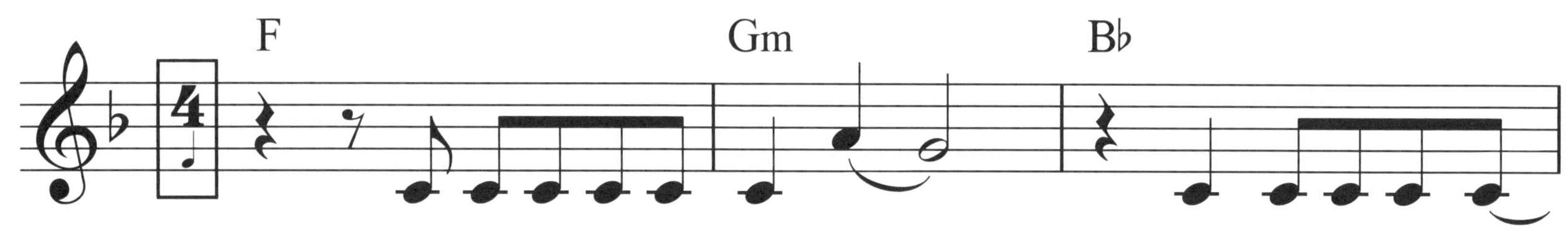

Gm
B♭
came, yeah, I can feel it in___ my veins. Hey,___ yeah.___
F
Gm
B♭
___ So this is what it feels like,___ right place, the right___
F
Gm
___ time___ with you.___
B♭
1.
2.
The right place, the right___ time.___ Oh,___ ___ time.___

I Knew You Were Trouble
Words & Music by Max Martin, Taylor Swift & Shellback
© Copyright 2012 Taylor Swift Music/Sony/ATV Tree Publishing /MXM Music AB, Sweden.
Kobalt Music Publishing Limited/Sony/ATV Music Publishing.
All Rights Reserved. International Copyright Secured.
F C Dm B♭
4
1 & 2 & 3 & 4 &
F C Dm
'Cause I knew you were
B♭ C F C
trou - ble when you walked in, so shame on me now.
1.
Dm B♭ C
Flew me to pla - ces I've nev - er been, till you

2.
F
C
C
put me down. Oh, ___ now I'm
Dm
B♭
ly - ing on the cold,___ hard___ ground.___ Oh___ oh,___
C
F
C
Dm
___ trou - ble,___ trou - ble,___ trou - ble.___ Oh___
B♭
C
F
___ oh,___ trou - ble,___ trou - ble,___ trou - ble.___

Pompeii

Words & Music by Daniel Campbell Smith

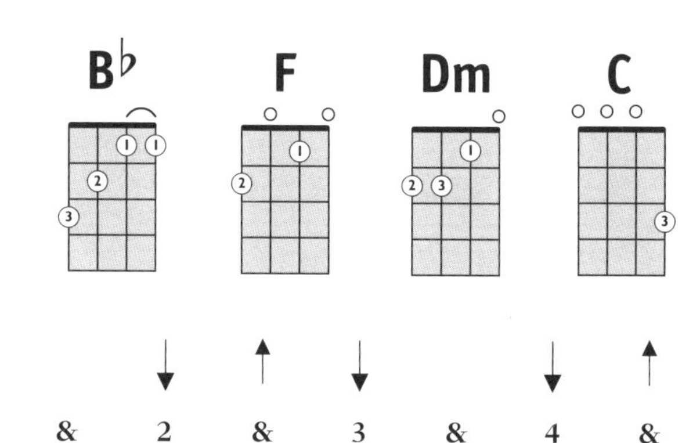

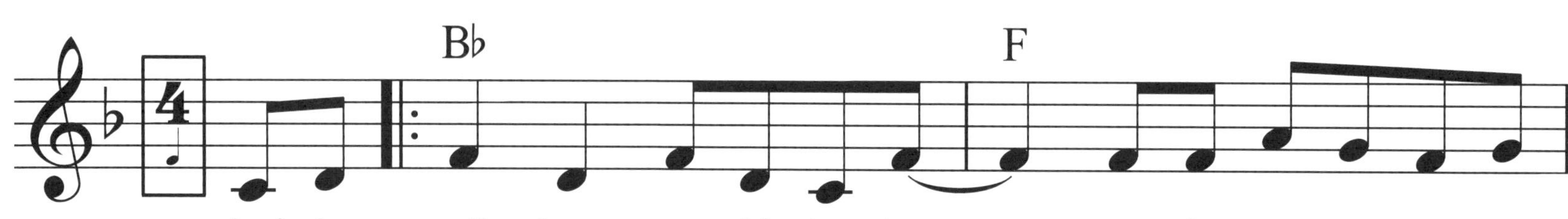

C
B♭
F
And if you close your eyes, does it al - most feel like you've
Dm
C
B♭
F
been here be - fore? How am I gon - na be an op-tim-ist a -
C
B♭
F
-bout this? How am I gon - na be an op - tim - ist a -
C
B♭
F
-bout this? Eh - oh eh - oh, eh, eh - oh eh - oh, eh,
Dm
1. C
2. C
eh - oh eh - oh, eh, eh - oh eh - oh. eh - oh eh - oh.

Let Her Go

Words & Music by Michael Rosenberg

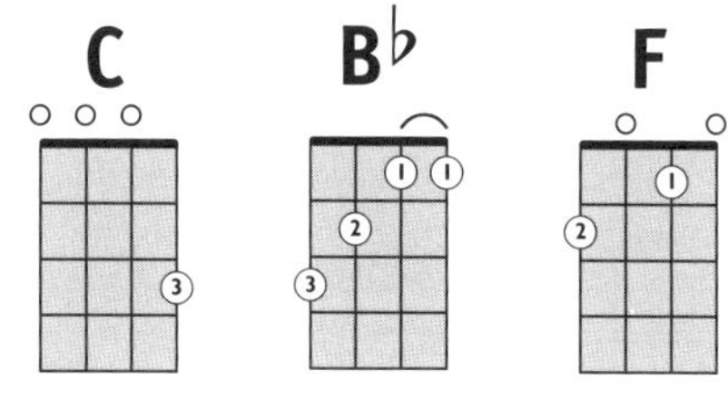

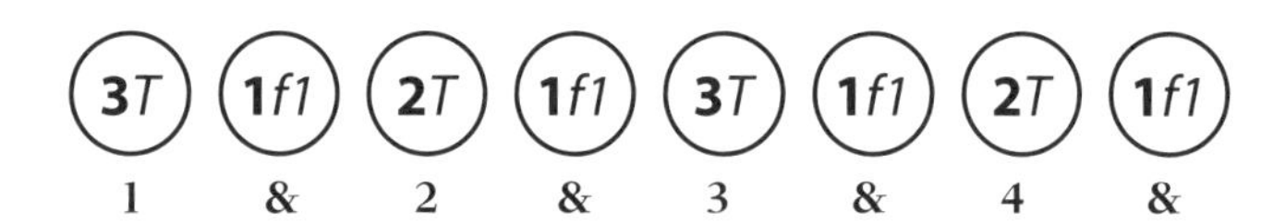

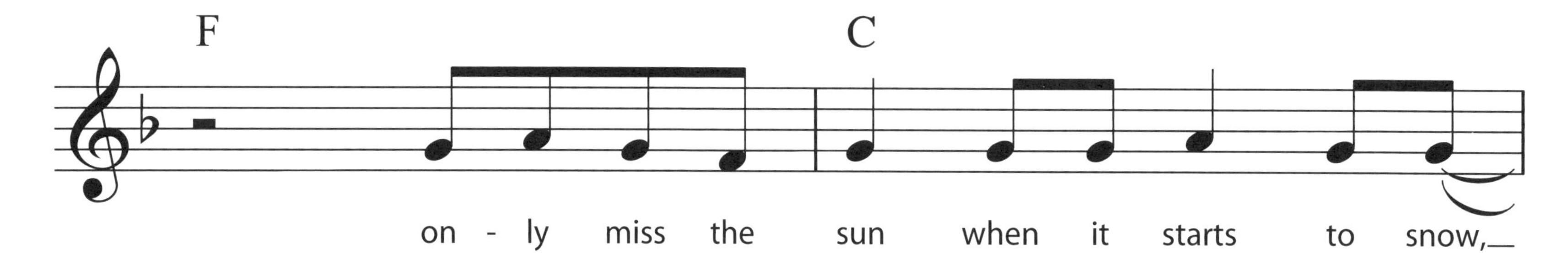

C
B♭
On - ly know___ you've been high when you're feel-ing low,

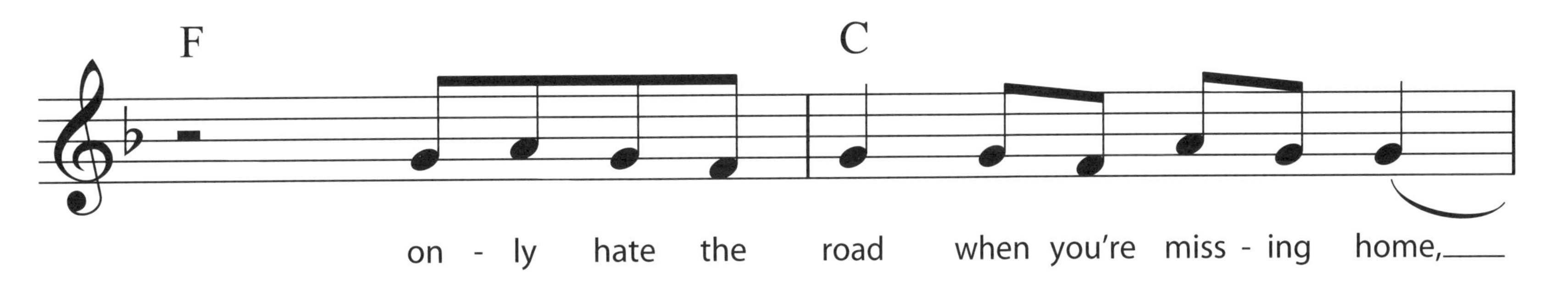
F
C
on - ly hate the road when you're miss - ing home,___

Dm
B♭
F
___ on - ly know you love her when you let her go;___

C
Dm
and you let her go.___

Wrecking Ball

Words & Music by Stephan Moccio, Sacha Skarbek, Lukasz Gottwald,
Henry Russell Walter & Maureen McDonald

Dm F C Gm B♭

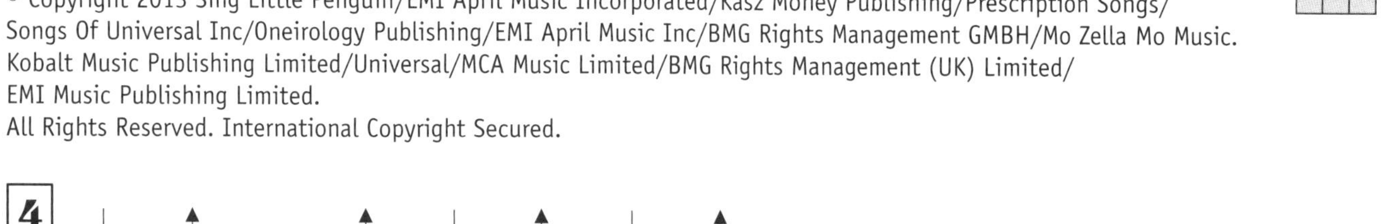

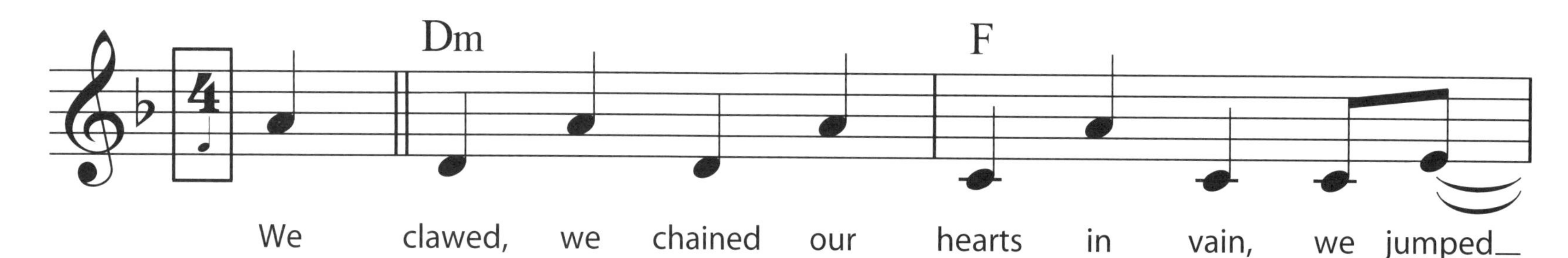

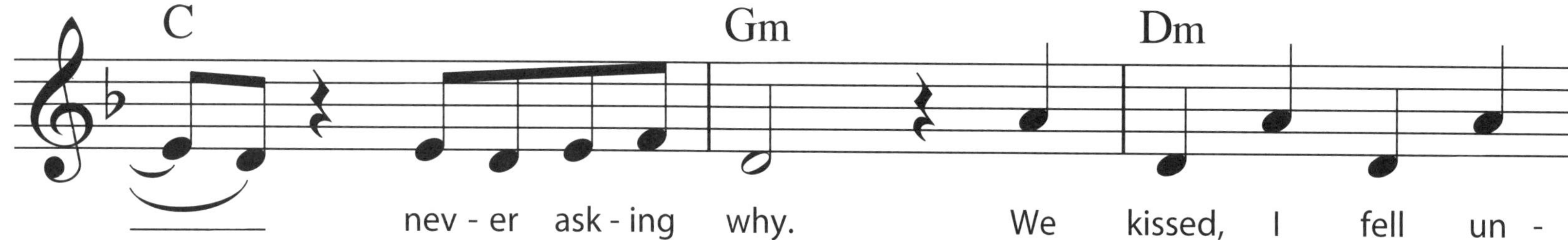

B♭
Dm
F
Don't you ev - er say I just walked a - way,
I can't live a lie, run - ning for my life,
I will al - ways want
B♭
F
you.
I came in like a wreck - ing ball,
C
Dm
B♭
I nev - er hit so hard in love.
All I want - ed was to
F
C
Dm
3
break your walls;
all you ev - er did was
wreck
B♭
Dm
3
B♭
me.
Yeah, you,
you wreck
me.

Burn

Words & Music by Greg Kurstin, Ryan Tedder, Brent Kutzle, Noel Zancanella & Elena Goulding

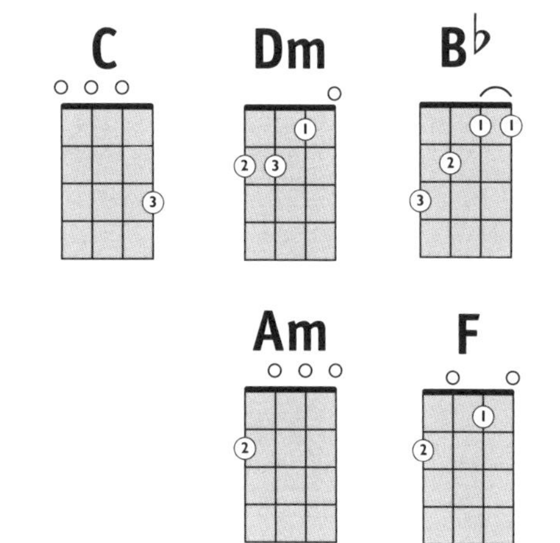

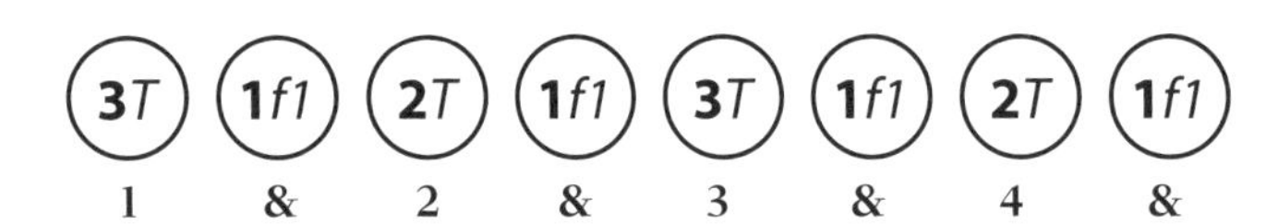

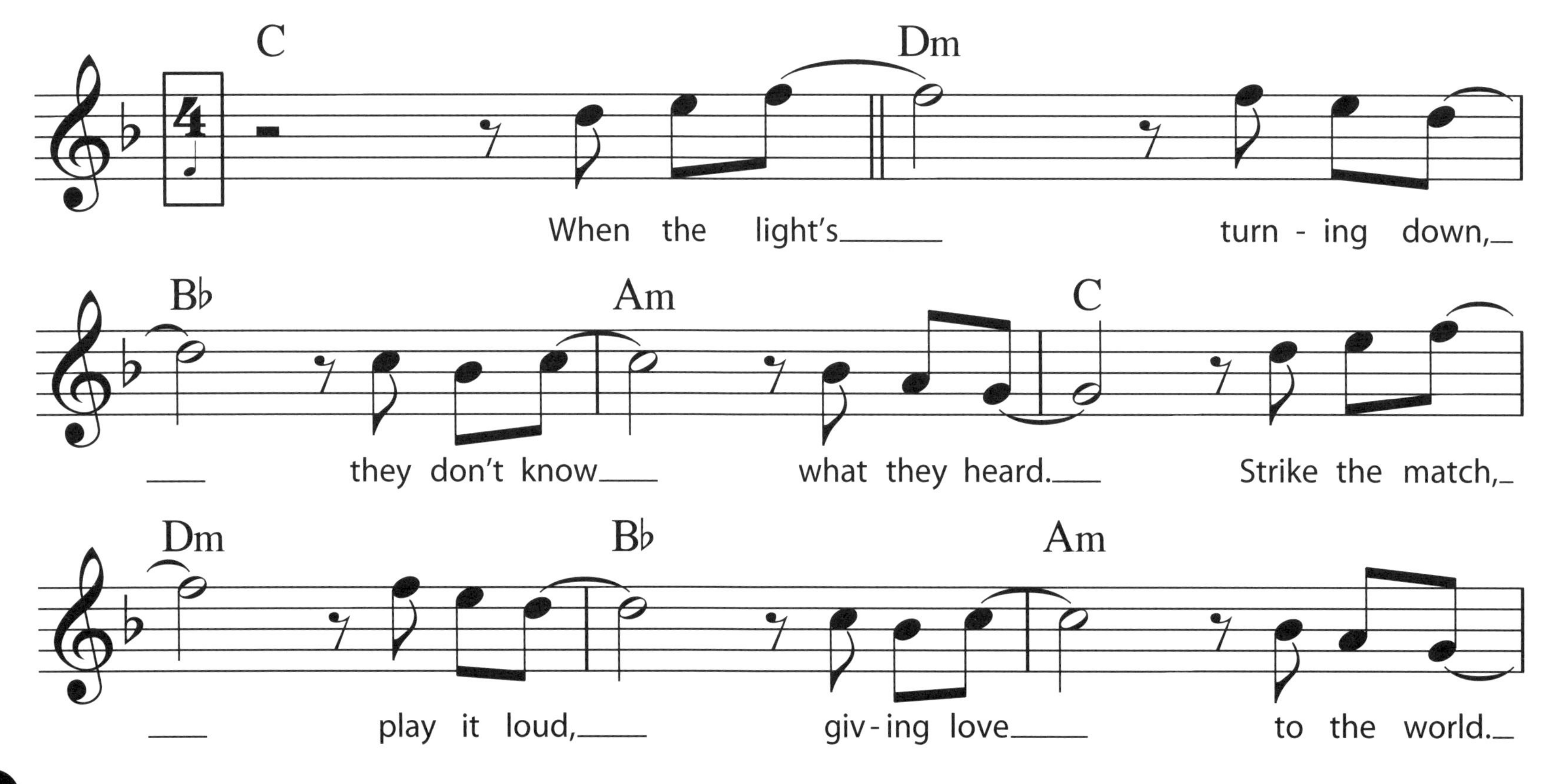

C
Dm
B♭
We'll be rais - ing our hands,
shi-ning up
F
C
F
to the sky,
'cause we got the fire, fire, fire,
B♭
Dm
C
'cause we got the fire, fire, fire.
And we're gon-na let it
Dm
B♭
F
burn, burn, burn, burn, we're gon-na let it burn, burn, burn,
1.
C
2.
C
Dm
burn. Gon-na let it
and we're gon-na let it burn.

...Baby One More Time
Words & Music by Max Martin
© Copyright 1998 GV-MXM.
Kobalt Music Publishing Limited.
All Rights Reserved. International Copyright Secured.
Dm A F Gm B♭ C
1 & 2 & 3 & 4 &
Dm A
Oh, ba - by, ba - by, how was I sup - posed to know
I should-n't have let you go,
F Gm A Dm
that some-thing was - n't right here?
and now, you're out of sight, yeah.
Show me how you want it
A F Gm A
to be; tell me ba - by, 'cause I need to know now what we got.

Dm
A
My lone - li - ness is kill - ing me,
F
Gm
A
I must con - fess, I still be - lieve.
Dm
A
B♭
C
When I'm not with you I lose my mind, give me a sign,
F
Gm
A
Dm
hit me ba - by, one more time.

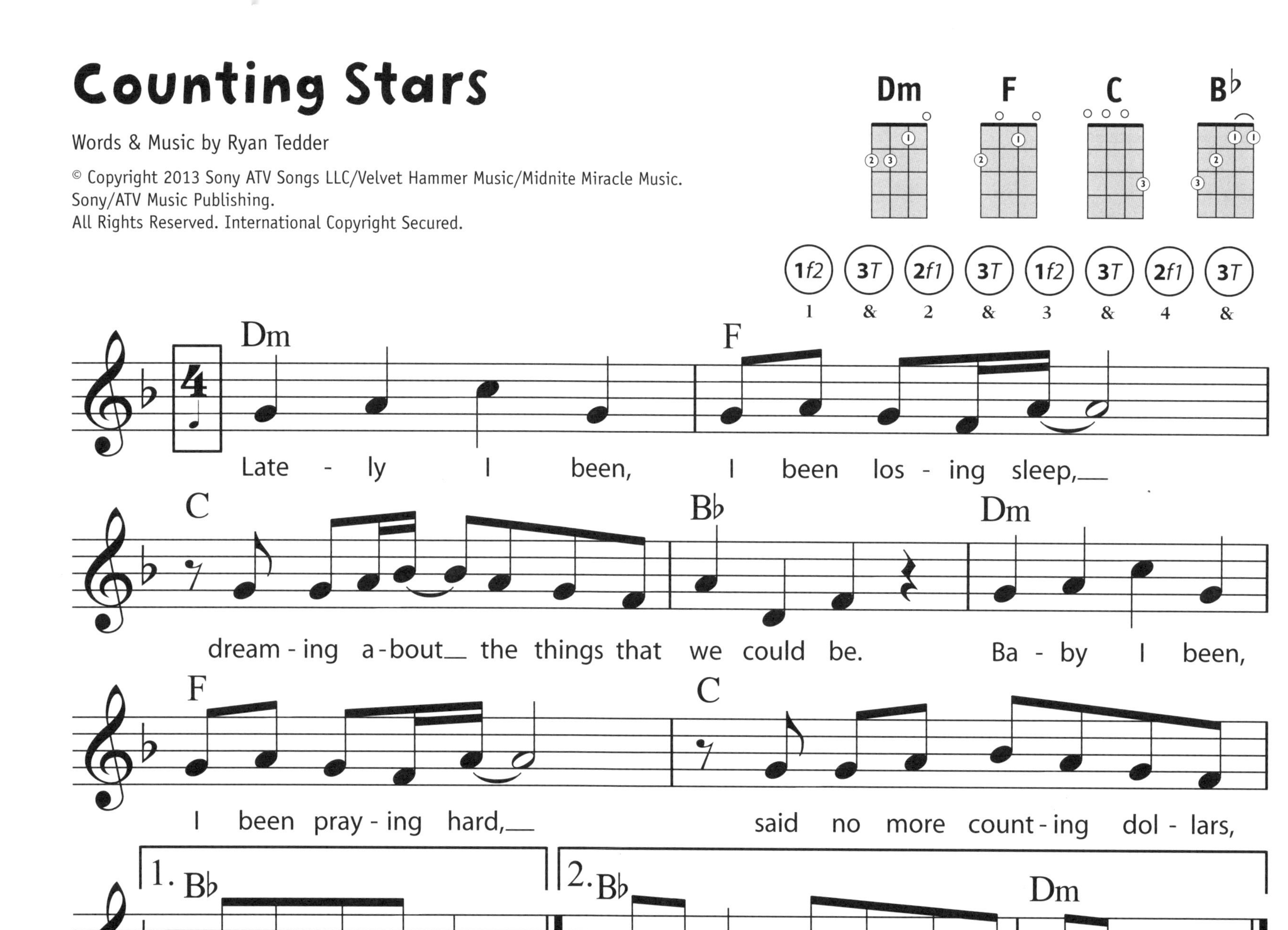
Counting Stars
Words & Music by Ryan Tedder
© Copyright 2013 Sony ATV Songs LLC/Velvet Hammer Music/Midnite Miracle Music.
Sony/ATV Music Publishing.
All Rights Reserved. International Copyright Secured.
Dm
F
C
B♭
1f2
3T
2f1
3T
1f2
3T
2f1
3T
1
&
2
&
3
&
4
&
Dm
F
Late - ly I been, I been los - ing sleep,
C
B♭
Dm
dream - ing a - bout the things that we could be. Ba - by I been,
F
C
I been pray - ing hard, said no more count - ing dol - lars,
1. B♭
2. B♭
Dm
we'll be count-ing stars. we'll be, we'll be count-ing stars.

1 2 3 4 5 6 7 8 9